SEPTEMBER 2016

SUNDAY	MONDAY	TUESDAY	WEDNESDAY	THURSDAY	FRIDAY	SATURDAY
				1	2	3
4	5	6	7	8	9	10
11	12	13	14	15	16	17
18	19	20	21	22	23	24
25	26	27	28	29	30	

OCTOBER 2016

SUNDAY	MONDAY	TUESDAY	WEDNESDAY	THURSDAY	FRIDAY	SATURDAY
						1
2	3	4	5	6	7	8
9	10	11	12	13	14	15
16	17	18	19	20	21	22
23	24	25	26	27	28	29
30	31					

NOVEMBER 2016

SUNDAY	MONDAY	TUESDAY	WEDNESDAY	THURSDAY	FRIDAY	SATURDAY
		1	2	3	4	5
6	7	8	9	10	11	12
13	14	15	16	17	18	19
20	21	22	23	24	25	26
27	28	29	30			

DECEMBER 2016

SUNDAY	MONDAY	TUESDAY	WEDNESDAY	THURSDAY	FRIDAY	SATURDAY
				1	2	3
4	5	6	7	8	9	10
11	12	13	14	15	16	17
18	19	20	21	22	23	24
25	26	27	28	29	30	31

DECEMBER

S	M	T	W	T	F	S
				1	2	3
4	5	6	7	8	9	10
11	12	13	14	15	16	17
18	19	20	21	22	23	24
25	26	27	28	29	30	31

JANUARY 2017

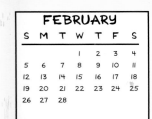

FEBRUARY

S	M	T	W	T	F	S
			1	2	3	4
5	6	7	8	9	10	11
12	13	14	15	16	17	18
19	20	21	22	23	24	25
26	27	28				

SUNDAY	MONDAY	TUESDAY	WEDNESDAY	THURSDAY	FRIDAY	SATURDAY
1 GANTAN-SAI MUMMERS' PARADE, PHILADELPHIA, PA NEW YEAR'S DAY — JOE ORTON B. 1933 FATHER GUIDO SARDUCCI B. 1943	**2** NEW YEAR'S HOLIDAY (UK & REPUBLIC OF IRELAND) HANDSEL MONDAY, SCOTLAND — CHRISTOPHER DURANG B. 1949 TODD HAYNES B. 1961	**3** HOLIDAY (SCOTLAND) QUADRANTIDS METEOR SHOWER HOLIDAY, NEW ZEALAND — LEON MCAULIFFE B. 1917 DABNEY COLEMAN B. 1932	**4** WORLD BRAILLE DAY — ANN MAGNUSON B. 1956 DAVE FOLEY B. 1963	**5** IROQUOIS WHITE DOG FEAST — MICHAEL O'DONOGHUE B. 1940 DIANE KEATON B. 1946	**6** ARMENIAN CHRISTMAS EPIPHANY — ROWAN ATKINSON B. 1955 KATE MCKINNON B. 1984	**7** CHARLES ADDAMS B. 1912 SAMMO HUNG B. 1952
8 AFRICAN-AMERICAN MEN GRANTED VOTING RIGHTS, 1867 — SOUPY SALES B. 1930 GRAHAM CHAPMAN B. 1941	**9** MARTYRS' DAY, PANAMA — GRACIE FIELDS B. 1898 BOB DENVER B. 1935	**10** VAUDOUN DAY, BENIN — WILLIAM SANDERSON B. 1948 JEMAINE CLEMENT B. 1974	**11** CHESTER CONKLIN B. 1886 ROSIE TRAN B. 1984	**12** MAHAYANA NEW YEAR (THRU 1/15) — JOE E. LEWIS B. 1902 JOHN LASSETER B. 1957	**13** SILVESTERKLAUSE, SWITZERLAND — CHARLES NELSON REILLY B. 1931 JULIA LOUIS-DREYFUS B. 1961	**14** PONGAL, INDIA — HAL ROACH B. 1892 STEVEN SODERBERGH B. 1963
15 FEAST OF THE LORD OF ESQUIPULAS, MAYAN PEOPLE — MOLIÈRE B. 1622 ANDREA MARTIN B. 1947	**16** MARTIN LUTHER KING JR. DAY — JOHN CARPENTER B. 1948 STEPHAN PASTIS B. 1968	**17** BLESSING OF THE ANIMALS AT THE CATHEDRAL, MEXICO — ANDY KAUFMAN B. 1949 JIM CARREY B. 1962	**18** OLIVER HARDY B. 1892 JASON SEGEL B. 1980	**19** TIMKAT, ETHIOPIA — RICHARD LESTER B. 1932 PAUL RODRIGUEZ B. 1955	**20** ATI-ATIHAN FESTIVAL, PHILIPPINES (THRU 2/22) — BILL GRIFFITH B. 1944 RAINN WILSON B. 1966	**21** INTERNATIONAL HOT & SPICY FOOD DAY — STEVE REEVES B. 1926 JEFF KOONS B. 1955
22 ROE V WADE DECISION, 1973 — JIM JARMUSCH B. 1953 DANIEL JOHNSTON B. 1961	**23** NATIONAL PIE DAY — HUMPHREY BOGART B. 1899 ERNIE KOVACS B. 1919	**24** ERNEST BORGNINE B. 1917 JOHN BELUSHI B. 1949	**25** BURNS NIGHT, SCOTLAND — VIRGINIA WOOLF B. 1882 ALICIA KEYS B. 1981	**26** AUSTRALIA DAY, AUSTRALIA — JULES FEIFFER B. 1929 ELLEN DEGENERES B. 1958	**27** THOMAS CRAPPER DAY — LEWIS CARROLL B. 1832 PATTON OSWALT B. 1969	**28** CHINESE NEW YEAR NATIONAL KAZOO DAY — ERNST LUBITSCH B. 1892 FRANK SKINNER B. 1957
29 W.C. FIELDS B. 1880 JERRY BUMPUS B. 1937	**30** BLOODY SUNDAY, LONDONDERRY, N. IRELAND, 1972 — SAUL ALINSKY B. 1909 DICK MARTIN B. 1922	**31** UP HELLY AA, SHETLAND ISLANDS, SCOTLAND — PAUL SCHEER B. 1976 BOBBY MOYNIHAN B. 1977				

FEBRUARY 2017

JANUARY

S	M	T	W	T	F	S
1	2	3	4	5	6	7
8	9	10	11	12	13	14
15	16	17	18	19	20	21
22	23	24	25	26	27	28
29	30	31				

MARCH

S	M	T	W	T	F	S
			1	2	3	4
5	6	7	8	9	10	11
12	13	14	15	16	17	18
19	20	21	22	23	24	25
26	27	28	29	30	31	

SUNDAY	MONDAY	TUESDAY	WEDNESDAY	THURSDAY	FRIDAY	SATURDAY
			1 AFRICAN-AMERICAN HISTORY MONTH BEGINS / VASANT PANCHAMI — S.J. PERELMAN B. 1904 / TERRY JONES B. 1942	**2** GROUNDHOG DAY — JANE WAGNER B. 1935 / TOM SMOTHERS B. 1937	**3** BEAN-THROWING FESTIVAL, JAPAN — TIM HEIDECKER B. 1976 / HANNIBAL BURESS B. 1983	**4** LOS COMANCHES DANCE, TAOS PUEBLO — DAVID BRENNER B. 1936 / ROB CORDDRY B. 1971
5 CHAMA CHA MAPINDUZI DAY, TANZANIA — CHRISTOPHER GUEST B. 1948 / CHRIS PARNELL B. 1967	**6** WAITANGI DAY, NEW ZEALAND / CONSTITUTION DAY, MEXICO — BOB MARLEY B. 1945 / ROBERT TOWNSEND B. 1957	**7** INDEPENDENCE DAY, GRENADA — EDDIE IZZARD B. 1962 / CHRIS ROCK B. 1965	**8** KITE FLYING DAY, KOREA — ROBERT KLEIN B. 1942 / CECILY STRONG B. 1984	**9** — ALICE WALKER B. 1944 / ZHANG ZIYI B. 1979	**10** PENUMBRAL LUNAR ECLIPSE / FENKIL DAY, ERITREA / TU BISHVAT BEGINS AT SUNDOWN — CHICK WEBB B. 1905 / MARK SPITZ B. 1950	**11** LANTERN FESTIVAL, CHINA — LESLIE NIELSEN B. 1926 / SHERYL CROW B. 1962
12 BURGSONNDEG, LUXEMBOURG — CHARLES DARWIN B. 1809 / ABRAHAM LINCOLN B. 1809	**13** WORLD RADIO DAY — PETER TORK B. 1944 / HUGH DENNIS B. 1962	**14** ST. VALENTINE'S DAY / MOREHOUSE COLLEGE ORGANIZED, 1867 — FREDERICK DOUGLASS B. 1817 / SIMON PEGG B. 1970	**15** KAMAKURA (SNOW CAVE FESTIVAL) YOHOTO, JAPAN — HARVEY KORMAN B. 1927 / CHRIS FARLEY B. 1964	**16** INDEPENDENCE DAY, LITHUANIA — EDGAR BERGEN B. 1903 / KEVIN ALLISON B. 1970	**17** CRAZY CHILI SHOWDOWN, MINERAL WELLS, TX (THRU 2/19) — DAME EDNA B. 1934 / HUEY NEWTON B. 1942	**18** INDEPENDENCE DAY, THE GAMBIA — GAHAN WILSON B. 1930 / IKE BARINHOLTZ B. 1977
19 JAPANESE INTERNMENT, 1942 — DAVID GARRICK B. 1717 / CARSON MCCULLERS B. 1917	**20** PRESIDENTS' DAY — KURT COBAIN B. 1967 / CHELSEA PERETTI B. 1978	**21** INTERNATIONAL MOTHER LANGUAGE DAY — NICOLE PARKER B. 1978 / JORDAN PEELE B. 1979	**22** — EDWARD GOREY B. 1925 / RACHEL DRATCH B. 1966	**23** TINCUNACO CEREMONY, ARGENTINA — W.E.B. DUBOIS B. 1868 / AZIZ ANSARI B. 1983	**24** FRENCH FRY FRIDAY, TRI-CITIES, WA / FLAG DAY, MEXICO — MITCH HEDBERG B. 1968 / CRISTA FLANAGAN B. 1976	**25** MAHA SHAVARATRI — ANTHONY BURGESS B. 1917 / RASHIDA JONES B. 1976
26 ANNULAR SOLAR ECLIPSE / JOE CAIN DAY, MOBILE, AL / CARNIVAL BEGINS, BRASIL — TEX AVERY B. 1908 / JACKIE GLEASON B. 1916	**27** STREET URCHINS' CARNIVAL, DENMARK / EASTERN ORTHODOX LENT BEGINS — PETER DEVRIES B. 1910 / WENDY LIEBMAN B. 1961	**28** MARDI GRAS — ZERO MOSTEL B. 1915 / LEMONY SNICKET B. 1970				

MARCH 2017

FEBRUARY

S	M	T	W	T	F	S
			1	2	3	4
5	6	7	8	9	10	11
12	13	14	15	16	17	18
19	20	21	22	23	24	25
26	27	28				

APRIL

S	M	T	W	T	F	S
						1
2	3	4	5	6	7	8
9	10	11	12	13	14	15
16	17	18	19	20	21	22
23	24	25	26	27	28	29
30						

SUNDAY	MONDAY	TUESDAY	WEDNESDAY	THURSDAY	FRIDAY	SATURDAY
			1 ST. DAVID'S DAY (WALES) / ASH WEDNESDAY / WOMEN'S HISTORY MONTH BEGINS — WILLIAM M. GAINES B. 1922 / BURNING SPEAR B. 1945	**2** HOWARD UNIVERSITY CHARTERED, 1867 / PUERTO RICO TERRITORY CREATED, 1917 — DESI ARNAZ B. 1917 / LARAINE NEWMAN B. 1952	**3** WORLD WILDLIFE DAY — RONALD SEARLE B. 1920 / TIM KAZURINSKY B. 1950	**4** FROZEN DEAD GUY DAYS, NEDERLAND, CO — PHILIPPE GAULIER B. 1943 / CATHERINE O'HARA B. 1954
5 BAIKAL INTERNATIONAL ICE RUNNING MARATHON, RUSSIA — ROSA LUXEMBURG B. 1871 / MATT LUCAS B. 1974	**6** PULASKI DAY, ILLINOIS — LOU COSTELLO B. 1906 / WILL EISNER B. 1917	**7** — WANDA SYKES B. 1964 / JENNA FISCHER B. 1974	**8** INTERNATIONAL WOMEN'S DAY — ALAN HALE JR. B. 1921 / MICKEY DOLENZ B. 1945	**9** BARON BLISS DAY, BELIZE — DEL CLOSE B. 1934 / MARTY INGELS B. 1936	**10** JOUSTING THE BEAR, PISTOIA, ITALY — HARRIET TUBMAN D. 1913 / TONY MILLIONAIRE B. 1956	**11** NATIONAL SKI-JORING FINALS, RED LODGE, MT / PURIM BEGINS AT SUNDOWN — ASTOR PIAZZOLLA B. 1921 / DOUGLAS ADAMS B. 1952
12 MAGHA PUJA DAY — BILLIE "BUCKWHEAT" THOMAS B. 1931 / DAVE EGGERS B. 1970	**13** HOLI / COMMONWEALTH DAY, UK / CANBERRA DAY, AUSTRALIA — AL JAFFEE B. 1921 / ROBIN DUKE B. 1954	**14** CHAHARSHANBEH SOURI (IRANIAN NEW YEAR CELEBRATION) — ALBERT EINSTEIN B. 1879 / BILLY CRYSTAL B. 1948	**15** — JOE E. ROSS B. 1914 / SLY STONE B. 1944	**16** FREEDOM OF INFORMATION DAY — HENNY YOUNGMAN B. 1906 / ISABELLE HUPPERT B. 1953	**17** ST. PATRICK'S DAY HOLIDAY (IRELAND) — SHEMP HOWARD B. 1895 / PATRICK MCDONNELL B. 1956	**18** SAVE THE FLORIDA PANTHER DAY — EDWARD EVERETT HORTON B. 1886 / BILL FRISELL B. 1951
19 BUZZARD DAY, HINCKLEY, OH — MOMS MABLEY B. 1894 / NEIL LABUTE B. 1963	**20** SPRING EQUINOX (3:29AM, PDT) / BENITO JUAREZ'S BIRTHDAY OBSERVED, MEXICO — RAY GOULDING B. 1922 / CARL REINER B. 1922	**21** NAW RUZ / WORLD POETRY DAY — POCAHONTAS D. 1617 / VIVIAN STANSHALL B. 1943	**22** SAKA (INDIAN NEW YEAR 1939) — CHICO MARX B. 1887 / KEEGEN-MICHAEL KEY B. 1971	**23** WORLD METEOROLOGICAL DAY — AKIRA KUROSAWA B. 1910 / MARTY ALLEN B. 1922	**24** DAY OF REMEMBRANCE FOR TRUTH & JUSTICE, ARGENTINA — DARIO FO B. 1926 / TIG NOTARO B. 1971	**25** WURSTFEST, HERMANN, MO — FLANNERY O'CONNOR B. 1925 / ARETHA FRANKLIN B. 1942
26 MOTHERING SUNDAY (UK) / DAYLIGHT SAVING BEGINS / SEATTLE METROPOLITANS 1ST US TEAM TO WIN STANLEY CUP, 1917 — RUFUS THOMAS B. 1917 / BOB ELLIOTT B. 1923	**27** OSWEILER, LUXEMBOURG — CARL BARKS B. 1901 / QUENTIN TARANTINO B. 1963	**28** RAMAYANA (THRU 4/5) — RUSSELL BANKS B. 1940 / NICK FROST B. 1972	**29** — ERIC IDLE B. 1943 / AMY SEDARIS B. 1961	**30** — JOHN ASTIN B. 1930 / PAUL REISER B. 1957	**31** CÉSAR CHÁVEZ DAY — CESAR CHAVEZ B. 1927 / RHEA PERLMAN B. 1948	

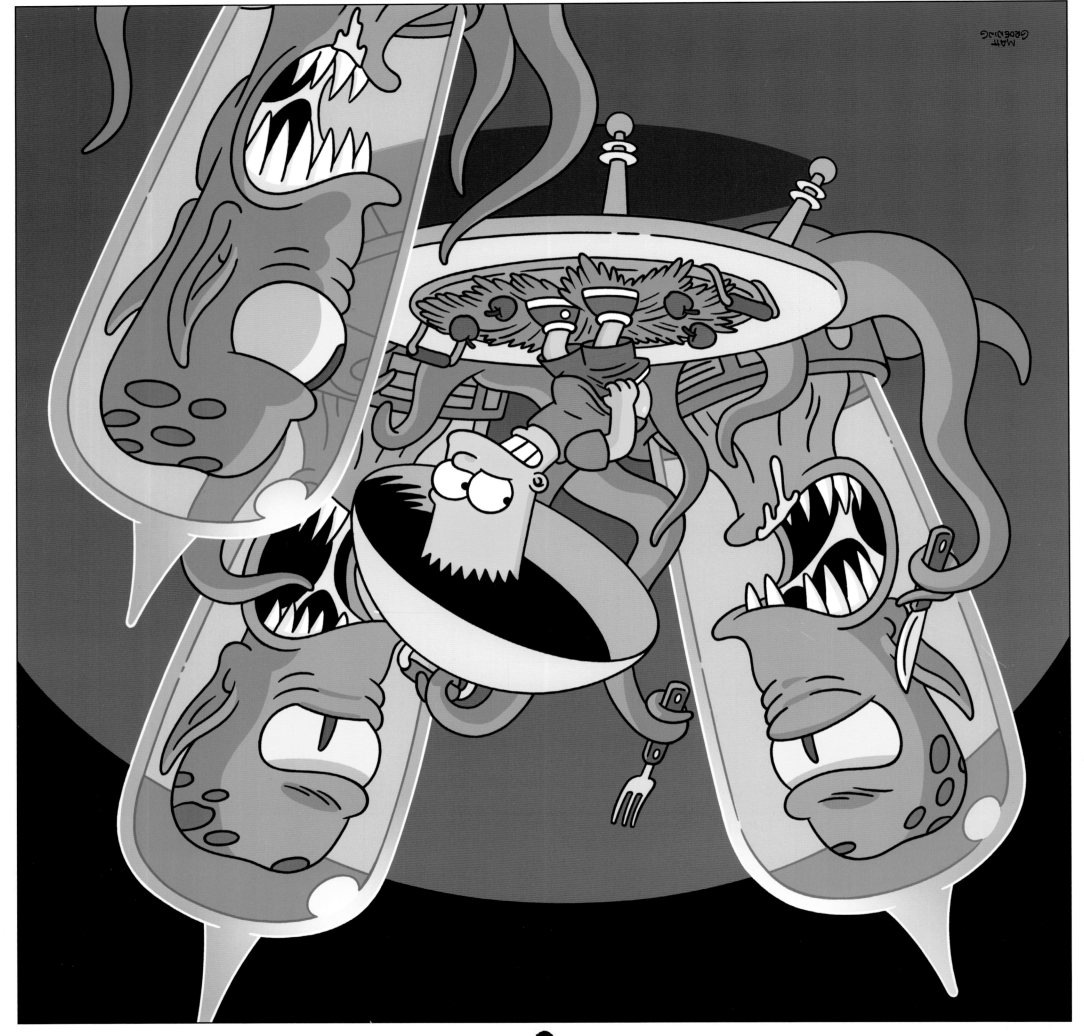

APRIL 2017

MARCH

S	M	T	W	T	F	S
			1	2	3	4
5	6	7	8	9	10	11
12	13	14	15	16	17	18
19	20	21	22	23	24	25
26	27	28	29	30	31	

MAY

S	M	T	W	T	F	S
	1	2	3	4	5	6
7	8	9	10	11	12	13
14	15	16	17	18	19	20
21	22	23	24	25	26	27
28	29	30	31			

SUNDAY	MONDAY	TUESDAY	WEDNESDAY	THURSDAY	FRIDAY	SATURDAY
						1 APRIL FOOLS' DAY TOSHIRO MIFUNE B. 1920 TARAN KILLAM B. 1982
2 CHILDREN'S BOOK DAY LOU MONTE B. 1917 MARVIN GAYE B. 1939	**3** TATER DAY, BENTON, KY MARLON BRANDO B. 1924 DAVID HYDE PIERCE B. 1959	**4** QING MING FESTIVAL, CHINA DAVID CROSS B. 1964 ERIC ANDRÉ B. 1983	**5** RAMANAVAMI ROGER CORMAN B. 1926 STEWART LEE B. 1968	**6** US ENTERS WWI, 1917 MERLE HAGGARD B. 1937 PHIL AUSTIN B. 1941	**7** RWANDAN GENOCIDE MEMORIAL DAY MONGO SANTAMARÍA B. 1917 ERIC WAREHEIM B. 1976	**8** CALIFORNIA POPPY FESTIVAL, LANCASTER, CA YIP HARBURG B. 1896 SHECKY GREENE B. 1925
9 FINNISH LANGUAGE DAY, FINLAND PALM SUNDAY TOM LEHRER B. 1928 AVERY SCHREIBER B. 1935	**10** MAHAVIR JAYANTI PASSOVER BEGINS AT SUNDOWN (THRU 4/18) HARRY MORGAN B. 1915 BUNNY WAILER B. 1947	**11** PASSOVER (PESACH) LOUISE LASSER B. 1939 BILL IRWIN B. 1950	**12** COSMONAUTICS DAY, RUSSIA TINY TIM B. 1932 DAVID LETTERMAN B. 1947	**13** RA-RA, HAITI DON ADAMS B. 1923 AL GREEN B. 1946	**14** GOOD FRIDAY (UK) DIA DE LAS AMERICAS, HONDURAS ALI AKBAR KHAN B. 1922 DANIEL CLOWES B. 1961	**15** FATHER DAMIEN DAY, HAWAII HANS CONRIED B. 1917 SETH ROGEN B. 1982
16 EASTER SUNDAY EASTERN ORTHODOX EASTER CHARLIE CHAPLIN B. 1889 SPIKE MILLIGAN B. 1918	**17** EASTER MONDAY (UK & REPUBLIC OF IRELAND) HALLATON BOTTLE KICKING, ENGLAND SEÑOR WENCES B. 1896 LIZ PHAIR B. 1967	**18** NATIONAL LIBRARY WORKERS DAY PIGMEAT MARKHAM B. 1904 CONAN O'BRIEN B. 1963	**19** FESTIVAL OF THE SARDINE, SPAIN DUDLEY MOORE B. 1935 WYATT CENAC B. 1976	**20** SUMARDAGURINN FYRSTI, ICELAND HAROLD LLOYD B. 1893 GEORGE TAKEI B. 1937	**21** FIRST DAY OF RIDVAN ELAINE MAY B. 1932 NICOLE SULLIVAN B. 1970	**22** EARTH DAY JACK NICHOLSON B. 1937 JOHN WATERS B. 1946
23 ST. GEORGE'S DAY (ENGLAND) MICHAEL MOORE B. 1954 JOHN OLIVER B. 1977 **30** MANGÉ LES MORTS CLORIS LEACHMAN B. 1926 BILL PLYMPTON B. 1946	**24** LAILAT AL MIRAJ (NIGHT JOURNEY) ARMENIAN MARTYRS' DAY HOLOCAUST REMEMBRANCE DAY JACK E. LEONARD B. 1910 CEDRIC THE ENTERTAINER B. 1964	**25** ANZAC DAY, AUSTRALIA, NEW ZEALAND ELLA FITZGERALD B. 1917 JOHAN CRUYFF B. 1947	**26** ADMINISTRATIVE PROFESSIONALS DAY I.M. PEI B. 1917 CAROL BURNETT B. 1933	**27** HORSE DAY, TURKMENISTAN WALTER LANTZ B. 1899 AUGUST WILSON B. 1945	**28** NEW ORLEANS JAZZ FEST BEGINS (THRU 5/7) CAROLYN JONES B. 1930 CAROLYN FORCHÉ B. 1950	**29** CHENG CHENG KUNG LANDING DAY, TAIWAN MAYA DEREN B. 1917 CELESTE HOLM B. 1917

MAY 2017

APRIL

S	M	T	W	T	F	S
						1
2	3	4	5	6	7	8
9	10	11	12	13	14	15
16	17	18	19	20	21	22
23	24	25	26	27	28	29
30						

JUNE

S	M	T	W	T	F	S
				1	2	3
4	5	6	7	8	9	10
11	12	13	14	15	16	17
18	19	20	21	22	23	24
25	26	27	28	29	30	

SUNDAY	MONDAY	TUESDAY	WEDNESDAY	THURSDAY	FRIDAY	SATURDAY
	1 YOM HA'ATZMAUT / INTERNATIONAL WORKERS DAY / LABOR DAY, MEXICO / MAY DAY HOLIDAY (UK & REPUBLIC OF IRELAND) JOSEPH HELLER B. 1923 / JOANNA LUMLEY B. 1946	**2** TWELFTH DAY OF RIDVAN SATYAJIT RAY B. 1921 / ELLIE KEMPER B. 1980	**3** WORLD PRESS FREEDOM DAY ANN B. DAVIS B. 1926 / JAMES BROWN B. 1933	**4** CASSINGA DAY, NAMIBIA / NATIONAL DAY OF PRAYER ANA GASTEYER B. 1967 / WILL ARNETT B. 1970	**5** BATTLE OF PUEBLA DAY, MEXICO / INTERNATIONAL TUBA DAY NELLIE BLY B. 1867 / MICHAEL PALIN B. 1943	**6** CRAWFISH FESTIVAL, BREAUX BRIDGE, LA ORSON WELLES B. 1915 / GEORGE CLOONEY B. 1961
7 RADIO DAY, RUSSIA ROBERTA GREGORY B. 1953 / AIDY BRYANT B. 1987	**8** STORK DAY, RIBE, DENMARK THOMAS PYNCHON B. 1937 / RODDY DOYLE B. 1958	**9** GLENDA JACKSON B. 1936 / CANDICE BERGEN B. 1946	**10** GOLDEN SPIKE DAY, CORRINE, UT / MOTHER'S DAY, MEXICO DENNIS BERGKAMP B. 1969 / KENAN THOMPSON B. 1978	**11** BOB MARLEY DAY, JAMAICA PHIL SILVERS B. 1911 / MORT SAHL B. 1927	**12** LAILAT AL BARA'AH (NIGHT OF SALVATION) GEORGE CARLIN B. 1937 / BRUCE MCCULLOCH B. 1961	**13** LIBERACE PLAY-A-LIKE COMPETITION, LAS VEGAS, NV / LAG B'OMER BEGINS AT SUNDOWN STEVIE WONDER B. 1950 / STEPHEN COLBERT B. 1964
14 RICHARD DEACON B. 1921 / ERIC MORECAMBE B. 1926	**15** AOI MATSURI (HOLLYHOCK FESTIVAL), JAPAN L. FRANK BAUM B. 1856 / RALPH STEADMAN B. 1936	**16** CHESTER BROWN B. 1960 / KEVIN MCDONALD B. 1961	**17** BROWN V BOARD OF EDUCATION, 1954 "COOL PAPA" BELL B. 1903 / CRAIG FERGUSON B. 1962	**18** INTERNATIONAL MUSEUM DAY DON MARTIN B. 1931 / TINA FEY B. 1970	**19** CALAVERAS COUNTY FAIR AND FROG JUMPING JUBILEE (THRU 5/21) MALCOLM X B. 1925 / JOEY RAMONE B. 1951	**20** GREAT WALL MARATHON, CHINA / ARMED FORCES DAY DAVE THOMAS B. 1948 / ISRAEL KAMAKAWIO'OLE B. 1959
21 INTERNATIONAL REGGAE MUSIC WEEK BEGINS FATS WALLER B. 1904 / AL FRANKEN B. 1951	**22** HARVEY MILK DAY, CALIFORNIA / VICTORIA DAY, CANADA ARTHUR CONAN DOYLE B. 1859 / HARRY RITZ B. 1907	**23** DECLARATION OF THE BÁB MARGARET FULLER B. 1810 / MARVELOUS MARVIN HAGLER B. 1954	**24** ARCHIE SHEPP B. 1937 / BOB DYLAN B. 1941	**25** FLITTING DAY, SCOTLAND / KODIAK CRAB FESTIVAL MILES DAVIS B. 1926 / DEMETRI MARTIN B. 1973	**26** MULE DAYS, BISHOP, CA (THRU 5/29) / FIRST OF RAMADAN BEGINS AT SUNDOWN BOBCAT GOLDTHWAIT B. 1962 / MATT STONE B. 1971	**27** WORLD CHAMPIONSHIP KINETIC SCULPTURE RACE, ARCATA, CA RACHEL CARSON B. 1907 / JOHN BARTH B. 1930
28 FIRST REPUBLIC DAY, ARMENIA PAPA JOHN CREACH B. 1917 / LUCILLE KALLEN B. 1922	**29** SPRING HOLIDAY (UK) / MEMORIAL DAY / ASCENSION OF BAHÁ'U'LLÁH JOHN F. KENNEDY B. 1917 / AARON MCGRUDER B. 1974	**30** DRAGON BOAT FESTIVAL, CHINA / SPRING BANK HOLIDAY, UK / SHAVUOT BEGINS AT SUNDOWN MEL BLANC B. 1908 / BENNY GOODMAN B. 1909	**31** FRED ALLEN B. 1894 / CHRIS ELLIOTT B. 1960			

JUNE 2017

MAY

S	M	T	W	T	F	S
	1	2	3	4	5	6
7	8	9	10	11	12	13
14	15	16	17	18	19	20
21	22	23	24	25	26	27
28	29	30	31			

JULY

S	M	T	W	T	F	S
						1
2	3	4	5	6	7	8
9	10	11	12	13	14	15
16	17	18	19	20	21	22
23	24	25	26	27	28	29
30	31					

SUNDAY	MONDAY	TUESDAY	WEDNESDAY	THURSDAY	FRIDAY	SATURDAY
				1 GAY PRIDE MONTH BEGINS — NATIONAL ACCORDION AWARENESS MONTH — CLEAVON LITTLE B. 1939 — AMY SCHUMER B. 1981	**2** DONUT DAY — DANA CARVEY B. 1955 — WAYNE BRADY B. 1972	**3** MEMORIAL TO BROKEN DOLLS DAY, JAPAN — LEO GORCEY B. 1917 — CURTIS MAYFIELD B. 1942
4 FLAG DAY, FINLAND — HORATIO SANZ B. 1969 — RUSSELL BRAND B. 1975	**5** WORLD ENVIRONMENT DAY — BILL MOYERS B. 1934 — LAURIE ANDERSON B. 1947	**6** HARVEY FIERSTEIN B. 1954 — BJÖRN BORG B. 1956	**7** GWENDOLYN BROOKS B. 1917 — DEAN MARTIN B. 1917	**8** FRANK LLOYD WRIGHT B. 1867 — SCOTT ADAMS B. 1957	**9** JACKIE MASON B. 1931 — MICHAEL J. FOX B. 1961	**10** MAURICE SENDAK B. 1928 — KATE FLANNERY B. 1964
11 KING KAMEHAMEHA DAY, HAWAII — GENE WILDER B. 1933 — HUGH LAURIE B. 1959	**12** LOVING DAY — JIM NABORS B. 1930 — SCOTT THOMPSON B. 1959	**13** MINERS UNION DAY, BUTTE, MT — PAUL LYNDE B. 1926 — LAURA KIGHTLINGER B. 1969	**14** WORLD BLOOD DONOR DAY — FLAG DAY — JEREMY DYSON B. 1966 — STEFFI GRAF B. 1969	**15** DEVIL DANCERS OF VENEZUELA — LASH LARUE B. 1917 — NEIL PATRICK HARRIS B. 1973	**16** BLOOMSDAY — STAN LAUREL B. 1890 — ABBY ELLIOT B. 1987	**17** NATIONAL HOLLERIN' CONTEST, SPIVEY'S CORNER, NC — IGOR STRAVINSKY B. 1882 — WILL FORTE B. 1970
18 FATHER'S DAY — EL COLACHO BABY-JUMPING FESTIVAL, CASTRILLO DE MURCIA, SPAIN — ROGER EBERT B. 1942 — CAROL KANE B. 1952	**19** JUNETEENTH — MOE HOWARD B. 1897 — GENA ROWLANDS B. 1930	**20** SUMMER SOLSTICE (9:25PM, PDT) — WORLD JUGGLING DAY — BRIAN WILSON B. 1942 — JOHN GOODMAN B. 1952	**21** LONGEST DAY — FIRST NATIONS DAY, CANADA — JOE FLAHERTY B. 1940 — BERKE BREATHED B. 1957	**22** LAILAT AL KADR (NIGHT OF POWER) — BILLY WILDER B. 1906 — STEPHEN CHOW B. 1962	**23** LANJARÓN FESTIVAL OF WATER AND HAM, SPAIN — WILMA RUDOLPH B. 1940 — FRANCES MCDORMAND B. 1957	**24** BULLWHACKER DAYS, OLATHE, KS — ST. JEAN BAPTISTE DAY, QUEBEC — AMBROSE BIERCE B. 1842 — MINDY KALING B. 1979
25 GAY PRIDE DAY — DAY OF THE SEAFARER — (EID) AL FITR BEGINS AT SUNDOWN (THRU 6/28) — CLIFTON CHENIER B. 1925 — RICKY GERVAIS B. 1961	**26** LUIS VALDEZ B. 1940 — MARK MCKINNEY B. 1959	**27** SATA-HÄME ACCORDION FESTIVAL, IKAALINEN, FINLAND — EMMA GOLDMAN B. 1869 — R.D. BURMAN B. 1939	**28** MEL BROOKS B. 1926 — GILDA RADNER B. 1946	**29** RICHARD LEWIS B. 1947 — BRET MCKENZIE B. 1976	**30** WHITE SWAN CELEBRATIONS, YAKIMA, WA (THRU 7/2) — LENA HORNE B. 1917 — SUSAN HAYWARD B. 1917	

JULY 2017

JUNE
S	M	T	W	T	F	S
				1	2	3
4	5	6	7	8	9	10
11	12	13	14	15	16	17
18	19	20	21	22	23	24
25	26	27	28	29	30	

AUGUST
S	M	T	W	T	F	S
		1	2	3	4	5
6	7	8	9	10	11	12
13	14	15	16	17	18	19
20	21	22	23	24	25	26
27	28	29	30	31		

SUNDAY	MONDAY	TUESDAY	WEDNESDAY	THURSDAY	FRIDAY	SATURDAY
						1 CANADA DAY, CANADA / TOUR DE FRANCE BEGINS / MYRON COHEN B. 1902 / CARL LEWIS B. 1961
2 DUCKTONA 500, SHEBOYGAN FALLS, WI / THURGOOD MARSHALL B. 1908 / LARRY DAVID B. 1947	**3** DEVIL'S PROMENADE, COMANCHE, KIOWA, & CREEK PEOPLES (THRU 7/6) / TOM STOPPARD B. 1937 / DAVE BARRY B. 1947	**4** INDEPENDENCE DAY / MARS PATHFINDER LANDS ON MARS, 1997 / NEIL SIMON B. 1927 / TRACY LETTS B. 1965	**5** / ROBBIE ROBERTSON B. 1944 / BILL WATTERSON B. 1958	**6** / DALAI LAMA B. 1935 / JENNIFER SAUNDERS B. 1958	**7** WINCHESTER HAT FAIR, ENGLAND (THRU 7/9) / MO COLLINS B. 1965 / JIM GAFFIGAN B. 1966	**8** TALKEETNA MOOSE DROPPING FESTIVAL, TALKEETNA, AK / KATHE KOLLWITZ B. 1867 / JEFFREY TAMBOR B. 1944
9 MARTYRDOM OF THE BÁB / ASALHA PUJA DAY / BASIL WOLVERTON B. 1909 / DAVID HOCKNEY B. 1937	**10** NUNAVUT DAY, CANADA / REG SMYTHE B. 1917 / BÉLA FLECK B. 1958	**11** / JOHN QUINCY ADAMS B. 1767 / E.B. WHITE B. 1899	**12** HOLIDAY (NORTHERN IRELAND) / HENRY DAVID THOREAU B. 1817 / CURLY JOE DERITA B. 1909	**13** OBON (THRU 7/15) / HARRISON FORD B. 1942 / CHEECH MARIN B. 1946	**14** BASTILLE DAY, FRANCE / WOODY GUTHRIE B. 1912 / ANGÉLIQUE KIDJO B. 1960	**15** PRINCE LOT HULA FESTIVAL, HONOLULU, HI / D.A. PENNEBAKER B. 1925 / FOREST WHITAKER B. 1961
16 FESTA DEL REDENTORE, VENICE, ITALY / BARBARA STANWYCK B. 1907 / WILL FERRELL B. 1967	**17** SWAN UPPING, LONDON (THRU 7/21) / PHYLLIS DILLER B. 1917 / WONG KAR-WAI B. 1958	**18** NELSON MANDELA DAY / CHILL WILLS B. 1903 / HUNTER S. THOMPSON B. 1937	**19** NICARAGUAN INDEPENDENCE DAY / MAX FLEISCHER B. 1883 / KELLY LINK B. 1969	**20** JAMBOREE IN THE HILLS, ST. CLAIRSVILLE, OH / CARLOS SANTANA B. 1947 / CARLOS ALAZRAQUI B. 1962	**21** YARMOUTH CLAM FESTIVAL, YARMOUTH, ME / GARRY TRUDEAU B. 1948 / ROBIN WILLIAMS B. 1951	**22** RAT CATCHER'S DAY / VAUGHN BODE B. 1941 / ALBERT BROOKS B. 1947
23 BIG ISLAND SLACK KEY GUITAR FESTIVAL, HILO, HI / RAYMOND CHANDLER B. 1888 / PHILIP SEYMOUR HOFFMAN B. 1967	**24** CHILDREN'S DAY, VANUATU / PATRICK OLIPHANT B. 1935 / JULIE KRONE B. 1963	**25** PAPA OGOU (ST. JACQUES LE MAJEUR) / WALTER BRENNAN B. 1894 / JOHNNY HODGES B. 1906	**26** CHINCOTEAGUE PONY PENNING / GRACIE ALLEN B. 1895 / STANLEY KUBRICK B. 1928	**27** SLEEPYHEAD DAY, FINLAND / NORMAN LEAR B. 1922 / MAYA RUDOLPH B. 1972	**28** HURRICANE SUPPLICATION DAY VIRGIN ISLANDS / MARCEL DUCHAMP B. 1887 / PHIL PROCTOR B. 1940	**29** ST. OLAV'S DAY, NORWAY / CHESTER HIMES B. 1909 / KEN BURNS B. 1953
30 / LAURENCE FISHBURNE B. 1961 / LISA KUDROW B. 1963	**31** TISHA B'AV BEGINS AT SUNDOWN / KAZ B. 1959 / B.J. NOVAK B. 1979					

AUGUST 2017

JULY

S	M	T	W	T	F	S
						1
2	3	4	5	6	7	8
9	10	11	12	13	14	15
16	17	18	19	20	21	22
23	24	25	26	27	28	29
30	31					

SEPTEMBER

S	M	T	W	T	F	S
					1	2
3	4	5	6	7	8	9
10	11	12	13	14	15	16
17	18	19	20	21	22	23
24	25	26	27	28	29	30

SUNDAY	MONDAY	TUESDAY	WEDNESDAY	THURSDAY	FRIDAY	SATURDAY
		1 INTERNATIONAL CLOWN WEEK BEGINS JERRY GARCIA B. 1942 TAYLOR NEGRON B. 1957	**2** ST. ELIAS DAY, MACEDONIA ISABEL ALLENDE B. 1942 KEVIN SMITH B. 1970	**3** JOSEPH SPENCE B. 1910 MARTIN SHEEN B. 1940	**4** TELLURIDE JAZZ CELEBRATION LOUIS ARMSTRONG B. 1901 BARACK OBAMA B. 1961	**5** NATIONAL MUSTARD DAY JOHN HUSTON B. 1906 JONATHAN SILVERMAN B. 1966
6 JOUST OF THE QUINTANA, ASCOLI/PICENO, ITALY LUCILLE BALL B. 1911 ROBERT MITCHUM B. 1917	**7** PARTIAL LUNAR ECLIPSE RAKSHA BANDHAN CIVIC HOLIDAY, CANADA HOLIDAY (SCOTLAND & REPUBLIC OF IRELAND) STAN FREBERG B. 1926 GARRISON KEILLOR B. 1942	**8** AUGSBURG PEACE FESTIVAL, BAVARIA, GERMANY DUSTIN HOFFMAN B. 1937 ROGER FEDERER B. 1981	**9** WORLD INDIGENOUS PEOPLES' DAY DAVID STEINBERG B. 1942 THOMAS LENNON B. 1970	**10** NATIONAL HOBO CONVENTION, BRITT, IA JORGE AMADO B. 1912 TOUMANI DIABATÉ B. 1965	**11** BURRY MAN'S WALK, S. QUEENSFERRY, SCOTLAND DAVID HENRY HWANG B. 1957 FRANK CAETI B. 1973	**12** PERSEIDS METEOR SHOWER ANNUAL CARROT FESTIVAL, CREANCES, FRANCE JOE BESSER B. 1907 CANTINFLAS B. 1911
13 ELVIS INTERNATIONAL TRIBUTE WEEK BEGINS, GRACELAND, TN ALFRED HITCHCOCK B. 1899 MERRILL MARKOE B. 1948	**14** SOCIAL SECURITY SIGNED INTO LAW, 1935 STEVE MARTIN B. 1945 GARY LARSON B. 1950	**15** KRISHNA JANMASHTAMI 15 AWA ODORI (FOOL'S DANCE), JAPAN (THRU 8/18) OSCAR ROMERO B. 1917 OSCAR PETERSON B. 1925	**16** HARMONIC CONVERGENCE, 1987 JULIE NEWMAR B. 1935 STEVE CARELL B. 1962	**17** INDEPENDENCE DAY, GABON MAE WEST B. 1893 THIERRY HENRY B. 1977	**18** MILWAUKEE IRISH FEST, WI ELAYNE BOOSLER B. 1952 ANDY SAMBERG B. 1978	**19** WATERMELON DAY, VINING, MN GENE RODDENBERRY B. 1921 WILLIE SHOEMAKER B. 1931
20 GABBY PAHINUI/ ATTA ISAACS SLACK KEY FESTIVAL, HONOLULU, HI H.P. LOVECRAFT B. 1890 DAVID WALLIAMS B. 1971	**21** TOTAL SOLAR ECLIPSE SAN MARTIN DAY, ARGENTINA COUNT BASIE B. 1904 USAIN BOLT B. 1986	**22** JOHN LEE HOOKER B. 1917 KRISTEN WIIG B. 1973	**23** 1ST ONE-WAY STREETS OPEN, LONDON, 1617 CORN PALACE FESTIVAL, MITCHELL, SD (THRU 8/28) GENE KELLY B. 1912 BRAD MEHLDAU B. 1970	**24** WILBERFORCE DAY, UK KEITH KNIGHT B. 1966 DAVE CHAPPELLE B. 1973	**25** WALT KELLY B. 1913 JEFF TWEEDY B. 1967	**26** PARYUSHANA PARVA (THRU 9/4) TED RALL B. 1963 MELISSA MCCARTHY B. 1970
27 HENLEY-ON-TODD REGATTA, ALICE SPRINGS, AUSTRALIA PEE-WEE HERMAN B. 1952 REECE SHEARSMITH B. 1969	**28** CHINESE VALENTINE'S DAY LATE SUMMER HOLIDAY (UK) JACK KIRBY B. 1917 JACK BLACK B. 1969	**29** ISABEL SANFORD B. 1917 MICHAEL JACKSON B. 1958	**30** ST. ROSE OF LIMA DAY, PERU ROBERT CRUMB B. 1943 MOLLY IVINS B. 1944	**31** WAQF AL ARAFA (HAJJ DAY) MARIA MONTESSORI B. 1870 VAN MORRISON B. 1945		

AUGUST

S	M	T	W	T	F	S
		1	2	3	4	5
6	7	8	9	10	11	12
13	14	15	16	17	18	19
20	21	22	23	24	25	26
27	28	29	30	31		

SEPTEMBER 2017

OCTOBER

S	M	T	W	T	F	S
1	2	3	4	5	6	7
8	9	10	11	12	13	14
15	16	17	18	19	20	21
22	23	24	25	26	27	28
29	30	31				

SUNDAY	MONDAY	TUESDAY	WEDNESDAY	THURSDAY	FRIDAY	SATURDAY
					1 (EID) AL ADHA BEGINS AT SUNDOWN (THRU 9/4) — CHEROKEE NATIONAL HOLIDAY, TAHLEQUAH, OK · LILY TOMLIN B. 1939 · STEVE PEMBERTON B. 1967	**2** NATIONAL FRISBEE FESTIVAL, WASHINGTON, DC · LAURINDO ALMEIDA B. 1917 · HORACE SILVER B. 1928
3 JOUST OF THE SARACEN, AREZZO, ITALY · MARIA BAMFORD B. 1970 · SHAUN WHITE B. 1986	**4** LABOR DAY — WORLD SEXUAL HEALTH DAY · RICHARD WRIGHT B. 1908 · WHITNEY CUMMINGS B. 1982	**5** FESTIVAL OF HUNGRY GHOSTS, CHINA · BOB NEWHART B. 1929 · WERNER HERZOG B 1942	**6** SOMHLOLO DAY, SWAZILAND · SERGIO ARAGONES B. 1937 · JANE CURTIN B. 1947	**7** MARION POPCORN FESTIVAL, MARION, OH · SONNY ROLLINS B. 1930 · CHRISSIE HYNDE B. 1951	**8** INTERNATIONAL LITERACY DAY · SID CAESAR B. 1922 · PETER SELLERS B. 1925	**9** FLAX SCUTCHING FESTIVAL, STAHLSTOWN, PA · OTIS REDDING B. 1941 · JOHN KRICFALUSI B. 1955
10 WORLD SUICIDE PREVENTION DAY — GRANDPARENTS DAY · RAYMOND SCOTT B. 1908 · ALISON BECHDEL B. 1960	**11** HORN DANCE, ABBOT'S BROMLEY, ENGLAND — PATRIOT DAY · JESSICA MITFORD B. 1917 · BRAD BIRD B. 1957	**12** PROCREATION DAY, ULYANOVSK, RUSSIA · LOUIS CK B. 1967 · PAUL F. TOMPKINS B. 1968	**13** PENDLETON ROUNDUP (THRU 9/17) · BILL MONROE B. 1911 · ROALD DAHL B. 1916	**14** MARGARET SANGER B. 1883 · WALTER KOENIG B. 1936	**15** LATINO HERITAGE MONTH BEGINS (THRU 10/15) · ROBERT BENCHLEY B. 1889 · NIPSEY RUSSELL B. 1918	**16** MEXICAN INDEPENDENCE DAY · B.B. KING B. 1925 · AMY POEHLER B. 1971
17 U.S. CONSTITUTION SIGNED, 1787 · JEFF MACNELLY B. 1947 · BOBBY LEE B. 1972	**18** ZHANGJIAJIE INTERNATIONAL FOREST FESTIVAL, CHINA · JUNE FORAY B. 1917 · JASON SUDEIKIS B. 1975	**19** TALK LIKE A PIRATE DAY · ARTHUR RACKHAM B. 1867 · JIMMY FALLON B. 1974	**20** ROSH HASHANAH BEGINS AT SUNDOWN (JEWISH NEW YEAR 5778) · ANNE MEARA B. 1929 · GEORGE R.R. MARTIN B. 1948	**21** NAVARATRI (THRU 9/29) — AL HIJRA — ROSH HASHANAH (JEWISH NEW YEAR) · CHIEF JOSEPH D. 1904 · BILL MURRAY B. 1950	**22** FALL EQUINOX (1:02PM, PDT) — NATIVE AMERICAN DAY, CALIFORNIA · JOAN JETT B. 1958 · MATT BESSER B. 1967	**23** JOHN COLTRANE B. 1926 · ANI DIFRANCO B. 1970
24 OUR LADY OF MERCEDES, DOMINICAN REPUBLIC · PHIL HARTMAN B. 1948 · PEDRO ALMODÓVAR B. 1949	**25** WILLIAM FAULKNER B. 1897 · PHIL "SCOOTER" RIZZUTO B. 1917	**26** WINSOR MCCAY B. 1867 · NICHOLAS PAYTON B. 1973	**27** MESKEL, ETHIOPIA · CARL BALLANTINE B. 1917 · MARC MARON B. 1963	**28** TEACHER'S DAY, TAIWAN · KOKO TAYLOR B. 1928 · JOHN SAYLES B. 1950	**29** GOOSE DAY, LEWISTON, PA — YOM KIPPUR BEGINS AT SUNDOWN · MADELINE KAHN B. 1942 · IAN MCSHANE B. 1942	**30** DASARA — BANNED BOOKS WEEK BEGINS — ASHURA BEGINS AT SUNDOWN — YOM KIPPUR (DAY OF ATONEMENT) · BUDDY RICH B. 1917 · FRAN DRESCHER B. 1957

OCTOBER 2017

SEPTEMBER
S	M	T	W	T	F	S
					1	2
3	4	5	6	7	8	9
10	11	12	13	14	15	16
17	18	19	20	21	22	23
24	25	26	27	28	29	30

NOVEMBER
S	M	T	W	T	F	S
			1	2	3	4
5	6	7	8	9	10	11
12	13	14	15	16	17	18
19	20	21	22	23	24	25
26	27	28	29	30		

SUNDAY	MONDAY	TUESDAY	WEDNESDAY	THURSDAY	FRIDAY	SATURDAY
1 WORLD VEGETARIAN DAY YOUSSOU N'DOUR B. 1959 ZACH GALIFIANAKIS B. 1969	**2** WORLD HABITAT DAY LABOUR DAY, AUSTRALIA-ACT, NSW, SA GROUCHO MARX B. 1890 BUD ABBOTT B. 1895	**3** X-15 SETS PILOTED VEHICLE SPEED RECORD 4,534 MPH, 1967 HARVEY KURTZMAN B. 1924 STEVIE RAY VAUGHAN B. 1954	**4** MOON FESTIVAL, CHINA SUKKOT BEGINS AT SUNDOWN (THRU 10/11) BUSTER KEATON B. 1895 SUSAN SARANDON B. 1946	**5** LARRY FINE B. 1902 BERNIE MAC B. 1957	**6** IVY DAY, IRELAND CAROLE LOMBARD B. 1908 FRITZ SCHOLDER B. 1937	**7** TÜBINGEN DUCK RACE, GERMANY JOE HILL B. 1879 SHERMAN ALEXIE B. 1966
8 CIRIO DE NAZARE, BRAZIL HARVEY PEKAR B. 1939 MATT DAMON B. 1970	**9** THANKSGIVING, CANADA COLUMBUS DAY JACQUES TATI B. 1907 TONY SHALHOUB B. 1953	**10** KIVI DAY, FINLAND THELONIOUS MONK B. 1917 JAIME HERNANDEZ B. 1959	**11** NATIONAL COMING OUT DAY SHEMINI ATZERET BEGINS AT SUNDOWN JIM WOODRING B. 1952 MICHAEL J. NELSON B. 1964	**12** SIMCHAT TORAH BEGINS AT SUNDOWN DIA DE LA RAZA DICK GREGORY B. 1932 BODE MILLER B. 1977	**13** GUMBO FESTIVAL, BRIDGE CITY, LA BILL ODENKIRK B. 1965 SACHA BARON COHEN B. 1971	**14** CLIFF RICHARD B. 1940 STEVE COOGAN B. 1965
15 MATA HARI EXECUTED, 1917 P.G. WODEHOUSE B. 1881 FELA ANIKULAPO KUTI B. 1938	**16** WORLD FOOD DAY NATIONAL BOSSES DAY OSCAR WILDE B. 1854 ANDY KINDLER B. 1956	**17** BLACK POETRY DAY MICHAEL MCKEAN B. 1947 MARK GATISS B. 1966	**18** PERSONS DAY, CANADA HUELL HOWSER B. 1945 LINDSEY VONN B. 1984	**19** DIWALI JAPANESE PICKLE FAIR, TOKYO JOHN LITHGOW B. 1945 TREY PARKER B. 1969	**20** BIRTH OF THE BÁB WANDA JACKSON B. 1937 JOHN KRASINSKI B. 1979	**21** SWEETEST DAY DIZZY GILLESPIE B. 1917 URSULA K. LEGUIN B. 1929
22 EXALTATION OF THE SHELLFISH, PONTEVEDRA, SPAIN CURLY HOWARD B. 1903 JOAN FONTAINE B. 1917	**23** CHULALONGKORN DAY, THAILAND LABOUR DAY, NEW ZEALAND JOHNNY CARSON B. 1925 WEIRD AL YANKOVIC B. 1959	**24** UNITED NATIONS DAY SONNY TERRY B. 1911 KEVIN KLINE B. 1947	**25** PABLO PICASSO B. 1881 CRAIG ROBINSON B. 1971	**26** MAHALIA JACKSON B. 1911 BOOTSY COLLINS B. 1951	**27** 20K WOMAN SUFFRAGE MARCH, NYC, 1917 JOHN CLEESE B. 1939 ROBERTO BENIGNI B. 1952	**28** DOUBLE NINTH FESTIVAL, CHINA COLUCHE B. 1944 ANDY RICHTER B. 1966
29 NAIROBI MARATHON, KENYA DAYLIGHT SAVING ENDS ZOOT SIMS B. 1925 RALPH BAKSHI B. 1938	**30** HOLIDAY (REPUBLIC OF IRELAND) DICK GAUTIER B. 1931 PONCHO SANCHEZ B. 1951	**31** HALLOWEEN MARTIN LUTHER POSTS 95 THESES, 1517 ALI FARKA TOURÉ B. 1939 JOHN CANDY B. 1950				

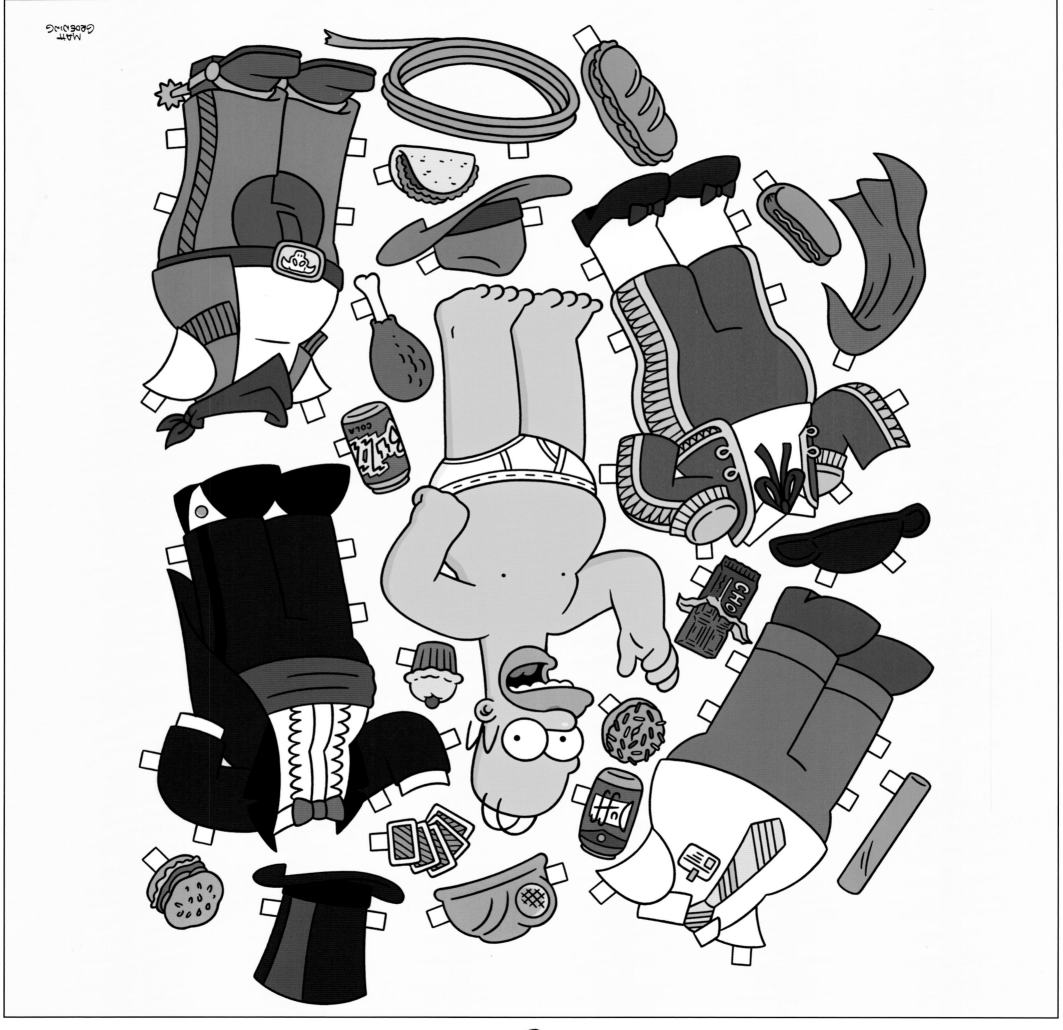

OCTOBER

S	M	T	W	T	F	S
1	2	3	4	5	6	7
8	9	10	11	12	13	14
15	16	17	18	19	20	21
22	23	24	25	26	27	28
29	30	31				

NOVEMBER 2017

DECEMBER

S	M	T	W	T	F	S
					1	2
3	4	5	6	7	8	9
10	11	12	13	14	15	16
17	18	19	20	21	22	23
24	25	26	27	28	29	30
31						

SUNDAY	MONDAY	TUESDAY	WEDNESDAY	THURSDAY	FRIDAY	SATURDAY
			1 INTERNATIONAL DRUM MONTH / ALL SAINTS DAY ZENNA HENDERSON B. 1917 TONI COLLETTE B. 1972	**2** DAY OF THE DEAD, MEXICO / ALL SOULS DAY GORSHON LEGMAN B. 1917 K.D. LANG B. 1961	**3** PUNKIN' CHUNKIN' CHAMPIONSHIPS, DELAWARE (THRU 11/5) OSAMU TEZUKA B. 1928 DYLAN MORAN B. 1971	**4** BIRTHDAY OF GURU NANAK DEV SAHIB WILL ROGERS B. 1879 WILLEM BREUKER B. 1944
5 GIANT OMELETTE CELEBRATION, ABBEVILLE, LA / GUY FAWKES NIGHT NATALIE SCHAFER B. 1900 SAM SHEPARD B. 1943	**6** SAXOPHONE DAY OLE OLESON B. 1892 MIKE NICHOLS B. 1931	**7** ELECTION DAY MARIE CURIE B. 1867 MORGAN SPURLOCK B. 1970	**8** JOURNALISTS' DAY, CHINA BRAM STOKER B. 1847 A.D. MILES B. 1971	**9** NATIONAL SCRAPPLE DAY DOROTHY DANDRIDGE B. 1922 KATE CLINTON B. 1947	**10** TURNIP LANTERN FESTIVAL, SWITZERLAND SCREAMING LORD SUTCH B. 1940 NEIL GAIMAN B. 1960	**11** VETERANS DAY / REMEMBRANCE DAY, CANADA, UK KURT VONNEGUT JR. B. 1922 JONATHAN WINTERS B. 1925
12 TREE FESTIVAL, TUNISIA / REMEMBRANCE SUNDAY, UK NEIL YOUNG B. 1945 MEGAN MULLALLY B. 1958	**13** HARVEST FESTIVAL, VIRGIN ISLANDS WHOOPI GOLDBERG B. 1955 JIMMY KIMMEL B. 1967	**14** NATIONAL PICKLE DAY WILLIAM STEIG B. 1907 VANESSA BAYER B. 1981	**15** DANIEL M. PINKWATER B. 1941 JESSICA ABEL B. 1969	**16** GREAT AMERICAN SMOKEOUT GEORGE S. KAUFMAN B. 1889 DIANA KRALL B. 1964	**17** VELVET REVOLUTION DAY, CZECH REPUBLIC PETER COOK B. 1937 DANNY DEVITO B. 1944	**18** ELEPHANT ROUNDUP, SURIN, THAILAND SOJOURNER TRUTH B. 1797 NASIM PEDRAD B. 1981
19 GARIFUNA DAY, BELIZE INDIRA GANDHI B. 1917 DICK CAVETT B. 1936	**20** REVOLUTION DAY, MEXICO DICK SMOTHERS B. 1939 SUPER DAVE OSBORNE B. 1942	**21** DR. JOHN B. 1940 HAROLD RAMIS B. 1944	**22** RODNEY DANGERFIELD B. 1921 TERRY GILLIAM B. 1940	**23** THANKSGIVING HARPO MARX B. 1888 ROBERT TOWNE B. 1934	**24** NATIONAL LEFTOVER AWARENESS WEEK BEGINS BILLY CONNOLLY B. 1942 STEPHEN MERCHANT B. 1974	**25** MANGÉ YAM (FÊTE DE LA MOISSON) WILLIE "THE LION" SMITH B. 1897 NEIL HAMBURGER B. 1967
26 CHARLES SCHULZ B. 1922 RICH LITTLE B. 1938	**27** ONION MARKET, SWITZERLAND BUFFALO BOB B. 1917 JIMI HENDRIX B. 1942	**28** ASCENSION OF 'ABDU'L-BAHA JON STEWART B. 1962 STEPHNIE WEIR B. 1967	**29** UNITY DAY, VANUATU GARRY SHANDLING B. 1949 CARL FINCH B. 1951	**30** ST. ANDREW'S DAY (SCOTLAND) JONATHAN SWIFT B. 1667 MARK TWAIN B. 1835